Garfield

Does Pooky need you?

JiM DAViS

ЯR

Ravette Limited

This edition first published by
Ravette Limited 1983
Reprinted 1984

———————————————————

Printed and bound in Great Britain
for Ravette Limited,
12 Star Road, Partridge Green,
Horsham, Sussex RH13 8RA
by Cox & Wyman Ltd,
Reading

ISBN 0 906710 08 1

GOBBLE! SMACK! SLURP!

JIM DAVIS 7-14

GARFIELD!

UH-OH

© 1982 United Feature Syndicate, Inc.

STAY RIGHT WHERE YOU ARE OR THE TEDDY BEAR GETS IT

JIM DAVIS   7-16

7-17

JIM DAVIS

© 1981 United Feature Syndicate, Inc.

© 1981 United Feature Syndicate, Inc.

© 1981 United Feature Syndicate, Inc.

© 1982 United Feature Syndicate, Inc.

© 1982 United Feature Syndicate, Inc.

© 1982 United Feature Syndicate, Inc.

GARFIELD, YOU'LL NEVER FIND HAPPINESS AT THE BOTTOM OF A COFFEE CUP

JIM DAVIS

9-29

I BEG TO DIFFER

LOOK, THERE'S SOME RIGHT THERE IN THE CORNER

BY GOLLY, YOU'RE RIGHT

© 1982 United Feature Syndicate, Inc.

SAY THERE, LITTLE LADY, WHAT ARE YOU DOING OUT ON A NIGHT LIKE THIS?

GOING FOR A STROLL

YOU'D BETTER STAY BY OLD GARFIELD'S SIDE. THE NIGHT IS FRAUGHT WITH PERIL

© 1982 United Feature Syndicate, Inc.

JIM DAVIS   7-28

THEY DON'T MAKE TREES LIKE THEY USED TO

11-25

OH NO!

JiM DAViS   © 1980 United Feature Syndicate, Inc.

© 1980 United Feature Syndicate, Inc.

FLICK

JIM DAVIS

FLICK

12-3

YOU KNOW YOU'RE BORED WHEN FLICKING A LINT BALL BECOMES ALL-CONSUMING

© 1980 United Feature Syndicate, Inc.

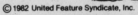

JIM DAVIS

4·5

IT LOOKS AS THOUGH I'M ON ANOTHER DIET

© 1982 United Feature Syndicate, Inc.

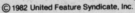

JIM DAVIS   6-2

© 1982 United Feature Syndicate, Inc.

JIM DAVIS

2-27

I WONDER WHAT GRANDIOSE DREAM GARFIELD IS HAVING RIGHT NOW

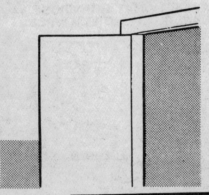

© 1980 United Feature Syndicate, Inc.

11-28

11-29   © 1980 United Feature Syndicate, Inc.

© 1982 United Feature Syndicate, Inc.

7-22

YAWN

WHAT HAPPENED TO YOU?

I GOT UP ON THE WRONG SIDE OF THE BED

JIM DAVIS

5-17

I LOVE IT WHEN YOU CUDDLE UP TO ME, GARFIELD

WHAT A WARM AND WONDERFUL GESTURE

MY NOSE WAS WET

JIM DAVIS 10-16

© 1982 United Feature Syndicate, Inc.

© 1982 United Feature Syndicate, Inc.

© 1982 United Feature Syndicate, Inc.

6-17

© 1982 United Feature Syndicate, Inc.

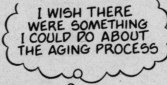

6-15

GARFIELD'S LAW:
CATS ARE NATURALLY ATTRACTED TO ONLY ONE TYPE OF HUMAN BEING...

JIM DAVIS

© 1982 United Feature Syndicate, Inc.

THE TYPE WHO IS ALLERGIC TO CATS

WAHCHOO!

GARFIELD'S LAW
CATS CAN'T HEAR COMMANDS...

GARFIELD! GET OFF THE BED!

JIM DAVIS 11-12

CATS CAN'T UNDERSTAND CAJOLING...

SEE? EVEN TOMMY THE CLOWN LIKES THIS NEW CAT FOOD

GARFIE

BUT THEY DO SENSE WHEN YOU WANT TO TAKE THEM TO THE VET

LET'S GO FOR A RIDE, GARFIELD

GARFIELD'S LAW:
CATS SHED IN DIRECT
PROPORTION TO THEIR
CONTRAST WITH A
PERSON'S SUIT

JIM DAVIS   11-13

© 1982 United Feature Syndicate, Inc.

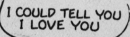

I MUST HAVE BLOWN A FUSE

FWIP

JIM DAVIS   10·5

ROWR

© 1982 United Feature Syndicate, Inc.

© 1982 United Feature Syndicate, Inc.

GEE, SINCE NERMAL ISN'T HERE, I'LL EAT HIS FOOD, TOO

© 1982 United Feature Syndicate, Inc.

5-24 JIM DAVIS

© 1982 United Feature Syndicate, Inc.

BLUT BLUT BLUT BLUT BLUT

WHEN ARE YOU GOING TO LEARN TO CONTROL THAT TEMPER OF YOURS, GARFIELD?

THE EXAC SAME INSTANT TH INVENT AN EAS POURING CATSU

6-5   JIM DAVIS

MINE!

POOKY IS A ONE-CAT TEDDY BEAR

OTHER GARFIELD BOOKS IN THIS SERIES

All these books are available at your local bookshop or newsagent, or can be ordered direct from the publisher. Just tick the titles you require and fill in the form below.

Prices and availability subject to change without notice.

Ravette Limited, 12, Star Road, Partridge Green, Horsham, West Sussex RH13 8RA

Please send cheque or postal order, and allow the following for postage and packing. U.K. 45p for one book, plus 20p for the second and 14p for each additional book ordered up to a £1.63 maximum.

Name ....

Address ....

....